LOOK AND FIND

Tasmanian Devil

**Illustrated by
Jaime Diaz Studios**

**Illustration scripts developed by
Tom DeMichael**

**Cover illustrated by
Rod Vass**

Published by
Louis Weber, C.E.O.
Publications International, Ltd.
7373 North Cicero Avenue
Lincolnwood, Illinois 60646

© 1995 Warner Bros.

Manufactured in the U.S.A.

8 7 6 5 4 3 2 1

ISBN: 0-7853-1186-6

PUBLICATIONS INTERNATIONAL, LTD.

Everyone in the Tasmanian Forest is busy getting ready for a big feast. Taz still has to go hunting for the juiciest, meatiest part of the feast's main dish, Carnivoral Carnival Stew. The helpers in the Tasmanian Gourmet's cookout kitchen are working up an appetite, so Taz had better hurry!

Can you find Taz, his friends, and these ingredients that they'll need to complete the recipe?

Cup of flower

She-Devil

"T"spoon of sugar

Half-cup of milk

Taz

"Pound" of cheese

"Table"spoon of salt

Tasmanian Gourmet

Brrrr! The North Pole is Taz's first stop on his quest for savory stew stuff. He has heard that a famous "snow bunny" has come up this way to do a little downhill skiing and Taz figures that he could use a little "fresh hare." But the rapid rabbit is having too much fun to join Taz for dinner.

Look for Taz, Bugs, and these other skiers on this North Pole ski slope.

Bugs Bunny

Little Penguin

Taz

Foghorn Leghorn

Daffy Duck

Pepe Le Pew

Elmer Fudd

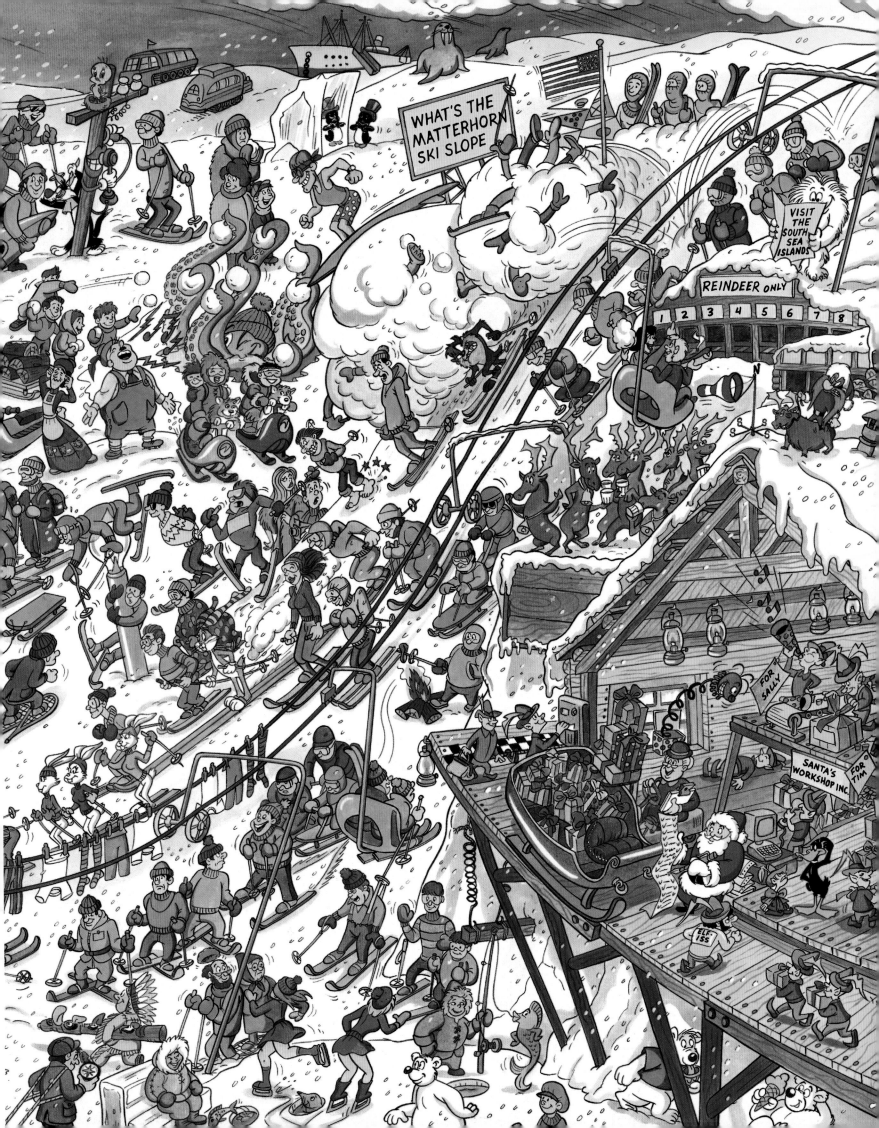

It's a jungle out there! Taz visits Africa where he would love to have Porky Pig for dinner. Porky, however, has no interest in *being* the main course. He's on a big-game safari himself.

Find Taz, then take a look and see if you can find Porky and his friends "hamming it up" in the jungle.

Porky Pig

Taz

Yosemite Sam

Bugs Bunny

Cecil Turtle

Mr. Gruesome Gorilla

Elmer Fudd

SAFARI SO-GOODY TRAVEL AGENCY

BLABOON

LIKE NEW !!!

FULL SIZE MODEL !!!

GREAT TRUNK SPACE

USED ELEPHANT LOT!

RACERS

We have achieved lift-off! Taz has headed up, up, and away, going where no Tasmanian Devil has gone before. The trek for a tasty entree has brought Taz to planet Mars, where Daffy Duck has been "ducknapped" by Marvin the Martian. Daffy is hidden amidst the fun of the Merrie Mars Amusement Park, so Taz will have a tough time finding him.

Look for Taz, then find Daffy and his planetary pals having fun at the Merrie Mars Amusement Park.

Taz

Daffy Duck

Marvin the Martian

K-9

Sylvester

Granny

Tweety

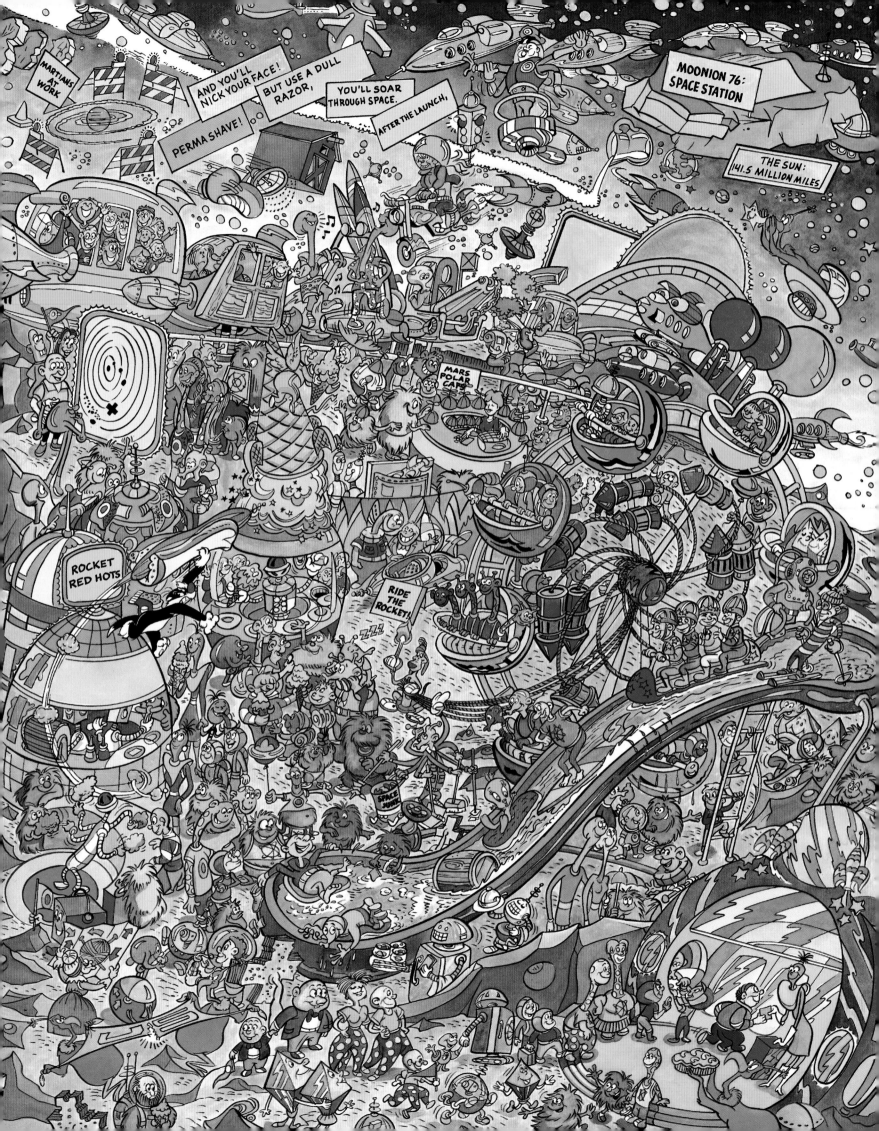

Howdy, pardner! Welcome to the wild and (sometimes) wooly West. After making a right turn at Albuquerque, Taz finds himself in ghostly Ghastly Gulch. He's got his eye on the Road Runner, but he needs to be faster than Wile E. Coyote to catch up with the fast-footed fowl.

Take a good look and see if you can locate Taz, Road Runner, and these ghost watchers in Ghastly Gulch.

Road Runner

Taz

Wile E. Coyote

Bugs Bunny

Witch Hazel

Yosemite Sam

The Three Bears

Going up! Taz is now moving on up to the Big Apple. He figures that Tweety may just be the sweet "tweet" he needs for his stew. Taz wants to nab him in this New York skyscraper. But it's a sure bet that wherever Tweety is, Sylvester is nearby. If Taz can catch that canary before Sylvester, he'll be sitting in the catbird seat.

See if you can spot Tweety and these other city slickers in New York City.

Tweety

Taz

Sylvester

Michigan J. Frog

Granny

Foghorn Leghorn

Goofy Gophers

¡Hola, amigos! Señor Taz has headed south of the border. He still has one thing on his mind: meat. Taz searches Mexico for a mouthwatering morsel of mouse, Speedy Gonzales.

While Taz is being needy of Speedy, see if you can find that macho mouse and his beach-goin' buddies in this busy Mexican resort.

Speedy Gonzales

Taz

Sylvester

Slowpoke Rodriguez

Daffy Duck

Claude, Sam, Babbit, and Catstello

M̲ais, oui! The pursuit has taken Monsieur Taz to the City of Lights, Paris. Time is running out, and Taz still hasn't been successful in finding the main ingredient for his succulent stew. Taz doesn't want to get "skunked," so he's looking for Pepe Le Pew among the artists and patrons at the Louvre museum.

Find Taz, then see if you can locate Pepe and his artsy allies as they appear with the famous art exhibits in and around the museum.

Taz

Bugs Bunny

Pepe Le Pew

Sylvester

Road Runner

Wile E. Coyote

Foghorn Leghorn

Your attention, please! Announcing the arrival of flight M-T-Handed with too-tired Taz as the pilot. Returning to the Tasmanian Airport would have been a bummer if it weren't for his friends who have planned a huge surprise party to welcome their ol' buddy home.

Now take a good look to find Taz, his friends, and the meat that got away in and around the Tasmanian Airport.

Taz

She-Devil

Sylvester

Bugs Bunny

Granny

Daffy Duck

Tweety

Go back to the cookout kitchen and find these things made out of chocolate chip cookie dough.

"Dough"nut
Sour"dough"
"Dough-dough" bird
"Dough"-a-deer
"Dough"berman pinscher
"Dough"zen cookies
Hair-"dough"
"Dough"ble-dip ice cream cone

Go back to the North Pole and find these other poles.

Barber pole
Maypole
Flagpole
Polecat
Fishing pole
Telephone pole
Light pole
Totem pole

Go back to the jungle to find these other "tree" things in the dense forest.

Tree surgeon
Tree frog
Tree house
Tree party
Tree shrew
Family tree
Tree ring

Take another trip to Mars and see if you can find these stars, constellations, and galaxies.

The Milky Way
Pie-Cs (Pisces)
Capri-corn (Capricorn)
Air-Es (Aries)
Big Dipper and Little Dipper
Black Hole